Signe Johanne Rhode

WHY

Do I Have to Sleep?

**A sleep-inducing bedtime story about William
- Inspired by Mindfulness for Children**

Plus a guided good night relaxation technique for your
child in the back of the book

WHY Do I Have to Sleep? is part of the WHY series, which was
written to make everyday challenges with children easy and playful.

The series was written in collaboration with independent brain
researcher Kjeld Fredens and child psychologist Berit Lyhne.

WHY Do I Have to Sleep?
(original title HVORFOR skal jeg sove?)

Copyright© Signe Johanne Rhode
Illustrations and graphic design/layout: Anja Løfkvist
Graphic production: Sarah Møller Pedersen
Translation from Danish into English: Pamela Starbird

ISBN: 978-0-9992579-3-7

Edition: 1st edition in English

Printing
Make Your Mark Global, LTD USA & Monaco
Printing in the USA & UK

Books in the WHY-series:
WHY Do I Have to Sleep?
WHY Do I Have to Brush My Teeth?
WHY Do I Have to Eat Veggies?
WHY Do I Have to Learn to Say Never Mind?

Foreword

This series of WHY books was written in collaboration with independent brain researcher Kjeld Fredens and child psychologist Berit Lyhne, who have shared their knowledge about how to engage children and effective methods that can be applied to make children feel at ease.

WHY Do I Have to Sleep? was written to help children to feel secure and positive about bedtime. The book is intended to help children calm their nervous systems, gain greater body consciousness and quiet their minds.

With inspiration from mindfulness techniques, the book helps children to fall asleep.

Guidelines for using the book

Children have different ways of calming down, and it is okay if it takes them a while to relax. What is most important is that you and your child have a cozy time reading together before bed.

Throughout the story, there are questions that you can discuss with your child about the importance of sleep. Involving the child in this way can support open-mindedness and help to develop an understanding of why getting enough sleep is important.

Guide your child to dreamland -
tips and tricks from experts

- **By doing something nice and relaxing just before bedtime** sleep can be associated with something pleasant.

- **Establishing rituals around bedtime is a good idea,** because predictability gives a calm feeling and a sense of security.

- **Items that the child can embrace or hold** such as a security blanket, stuffed animal, book or a picture, can serve as an anchor of security.

- The bed can more easily have a positive association if you **speak of it as an attractive place to be.**

- If children do not want to go to bed, it can be **nice for them to feel like they have some say in the matter.** This could be through offering them certain options, such as whether they would like to hold the white or the brown teddy bear.

- It might be best to review the events of the day with the child before it is time for your child to settle down; that way, **when it is time for the child to get in bed** and ready to sleep, **the focus is on relaxation only.**

- **Imagination and magic can also be used to make the child feel secure about sleeping.** For instance by "sprinkling" some "magical sleeping dust" over the bed encouraging the belief that it has the power to make you fall asleep easily.

WHY

Do I Have to Sleep?

**A sleep-inducing bedtime story about William
- Inspired by Mindfulness for Children**

In a small town in the countryside, William, Mia and Leo are running at full speed across the fields.

They look around, searching for something. William's legs are tired and his cheeks feel warm.

Then he stops. There is a sound! Now he can see something moving in the wet grass.

"I found it," shouts William with excitement.

Mia and Leo hurry over to William, who is smiling with pride. He is holding a little cat in his arms. The cat seems confused.

"There you are," shouts Mia in delight. She picks up her cat and hugs it.

Back home in front of the fireplace, William tells his mother and father about Mia's lost cat.

"How did you find it?" asks Mom.

"I was running around looking, and then I heard a sound so I stopped," says William. He crawls on the floor to show how he moved toward the cat so he would not scare it.

After they finish eating dinner, Mom says that it's time for bed. But William does not want to go to bed.

"Why do I have to go to sleep?" he asks.

"Because you need to get some rest," answers Mom.

"But I'm not tired!" William gripes.

Do you know why we sleep at night?

Mom tells him: "When you were out looking for Mia's cat today, you needed to use your whole body. You used your eyes to see it. Your ears to hear it. Your legs to run. And your voice for shouting. When you use your body, it gets tired. That's why you have to sleep at night."

But William does not understand. He just thinks that going to sleep is boring.

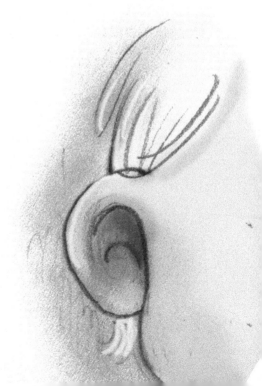

"So while I'm sleeping, my body gets charged up? Like when we charge my tablet?" William laughs when they are washing up in the bathroom.

"Yes. When you get your sleep at night, your body and mind are fresh again in the morning. They get charged, just like when we charge our phones or tablets," his Mom smiles, and hands William a pajama top that he pulls over his head.

Then she opens the window in the bathroom so William can wave goodnight to Mia and Leo. They live right next door. Mia is already at the window waiting for him.
Leo sticks his head out the window, too.
"Goodnight!" they wave with cheerful smiles.

Do you know anyone else who is also going to bed now?

When William is lying in bed, Mom tucks the soft blanket around him.

With a calm voice, she says, "Your eyes are tired after seeing so many things today. Your ears need some quiet. The day is done and there is nothing more you have to do today."

Then she kisses him gently on his forehead before she leaves the room.

How does it feel inside your body right now?

Soon William can feel that his body is a little tired.

He imagines a little caretaker at his feet who turns off a light.

The caretaker turns off the lights at his ankles and all the way up his legs, so the legs can fall asleep.

The caretaker continues to William's belly... his arms... and finally his head... He turns off all of the light switches.

The caretaker says goodnight to all of the body parts.

Doing this makes William's body feel calm and relaxed.

William can hear some low, familiar sounds coming from outside and downstairs in the living room.

A car driving past.
The voice of someone talking.
The spinning of the washing machine.

These are all sounds that he has heard many times before.

William thinks about when he found Mia's cat earlier that day. Thoughts begin to fill his mind and then his body starts to move around again.

Then William begins to imagine that he is filling his body with fresh air every time he takes in a breath. He calmly breathes in deeply, and each time he breathes out again, all of those thoughts are blown away.

The thoughts float upward to the clouds. That's enough thinking for today, he says to himself. If there are thoughts I want to think about, I can bring them back from the clouds any time I choose.

William blows his thoughts out of his mind each time he breathes out, until they become like little stars high in the sky.

The blanket is tucked around William from his chin to his feet.

Now his feet and legs relax. They calm down, feel heavy, and become perfectly still. It feels good for his toes, feet and legs to rest. It's as if William's toes whisper to him, "Thank you for letting us rest."

Now William turns his attention to his belly. It seems very soft and tender. He feels his arms getting heavy.

Good night, arms, William thinks.
You can rest now.

William lets his head rest on the pillow. His head feels heavy and William does not want to move it. He keeps his head still, relaxed on the soft pillow.

He can feel his eyelids getting much heavier now. His eyes are so tired that he feels his lids close together and stay closed. His eyelids feel so heavy right now.

William's whole body feels calm and deeply relaxed. With each breath he becomes more tired. His breathing slows down and he takes long, deep, even breaths. He feels more and more calm and relaxed.

In the distance, he hears his mother's voice whispering, "Sleep well, Sweetheart..."

Sleep well – a guided relaxation technique for children

By being fully present, you can help to establish a sense of security and calm and help to make bedtime the best time of the day for your child. It might be a good idea to read the meditation aloud in a quiet voice with a lot of pauses, so that your child has enough time to reflect on and sense what it is you are describing.

Relaxation

Lie down and get in a comfortable position under the blanket. Are you ready? Let's begin.

Close your eyes so you can concentrate on what it feels like to lie on top of the mattress and underneath a blanket. Feel your body temperature. You are not too hot nor too cold. You feel just right.

Start by listening to the sounds around you in the room and in the house or apartment. Maybe you can hear sounds from a television in another room.

A washing machine. A conversation. The wind. Cars. You know all these sounds. They are just sounds and it is fine that they exist. These sounds remind you that you are in a safe place, where you are comfortable and loved. If there is a sound that you need to react to, your body will know that and will wake you up. Now it's the end of the day. There's nothing else happening, and nothing that you have to do today. You don't have to learn anything new or be good at doing anything else right now. You can just let go and take the night off.

Feel your big toes. Feel each of your other toes all the way to your little toe. Feel the soles of your feet. The tops of your feet. Your ankles. Maybe you can feel that they are still a bit restless from running earlier today? Each time you exhale, it helps your feet relax more and more, and helps them to sink deeply into the mattress.

Feel your legs. The backs of your knees. The fronts of your knees.

Feel your thighs and both legs. They have been moving fast all day long, but now they are getting ready to stay still. They are warm. Relaxed. And every time you exhale, they relax even more and sink a bit deeper into the mattress.

Feel your hips. Your bottom. The lowest part of your belly. Feel the area around your belly button. Your chest. Feel your heart quietly beating. Feel how your breath flows in and out and how it rocks your body from the inside. You do not have to do anything at all. Your wonderful body can do everything for you, even while you are sleeping. It's okay for you to just let go.

Feel the lower part of your back. The muscles in the middle of your back. Your shoulders. Feel your whole back. Feel your spine and the vertebrae that are linked like a string of pearls. And when you relax, there is more space for your back to settle into the mattress.

Feel how the upper half of your body is resting. Each time you breathe out, you sink a bit deeper into the mattress.

Feel your shoulders. Upper arms. Elbows. Forearms. Wrists. Feel your hands, and all your fingers. They do not need to do anything else today. Everything you have used them for today, they will be able to do tomorrow, and more. They can rest now and go to sleep.

Feel that your arms are warm. They stay still and are resting. Every time you breathe out, they sink a bit deeper into the mattress.

Feel your neck. Your throat. Maybe you can sense the pulse beating next to your throat. Your chin is relaxed. Your cheeks are soft. Your jaw is relaxed. The tip of your nose might feel a bit cooler when you inhale and warmer when you exhale. Your eyes are resting under your eyelids. Your ears can shut out all the sounds they do not need to listen to any more today. Your forehead is smooth. Your whole scalp is relaxed from hairline to hairline. Even your hair is relaxed.

Your mind is free from thoughts. Each time you exhale, your head sinks a bit deeper into the pillow.

Feel your whole body. You can no longer feel where the mattress ends and your body begins. That is okay. You are safe here and nothing can touch you. Imagine that you are being held in a pair of loving arms that are gently rocking you from side to side.

You fall asleep. Perhaps you are already asleep. But you are still aware of my voice. You are safe. You are loved and protected.

Have a good sleep. Sweet dreams.

Thanks!

I would like to express my gratitude to brain researcher Kjeld Fredens and child psychologist Berit Lyhne for sharing their knowledge during the development of this series.

Many thanks to yoga and mindfulness instructor Anne Mette Kærgaard Olesen for the relaxation meditation and inspiration for this book.